THE BLOOMSBURY BOOK OF
Love Poems

For Rebecca and Hannah
— the greats

THE BLOOMSBURY BOOK OF
Love Poems

SELECTED BY
BENJAMIN ZEPHANIAH

ILLUSTRATED BY
CHRISTOPHER CORR

BLOOMSBURY

First published in Great Britain in 1999
Bloomsbury Publishing Plc, 38 Soho Square, London, W1V 5DF

Individual poem details feature on the acknowledgements page situated at the back of this book
Copyright © Text this selection Benjamin Zephaniah 1999
Copyright © Illustrations Christopher Corr 1999

ISBN 0 7475 4417 4

Printed in England by St Edmundsbury Press

10 9 8 7 6 5 4 3 2

Contents

Contradictoria

I love you, I love you, I hate you,
I hate you, I love you, I don't.
I want you - I just want to hate you
I just want to love you, but won't.

You make me unhappy, I hate you,
I loathe you, and that is a fact,
Get out of my life or I'll kill you.
Hey, where are you going? Come back!

Don't leave me, I love you, I loathe you.
You're brutal, you're charming, you're me
You're my one and only, I love you.
Get out of my sight or I'll scream!

I love you, you're special, you're nothing
You're no one, you're someone quite dear
I hate you, I miss you, I love you.
I hope that I've made myself clear.

Cynthia Hamilton

9

The Jungle Husband

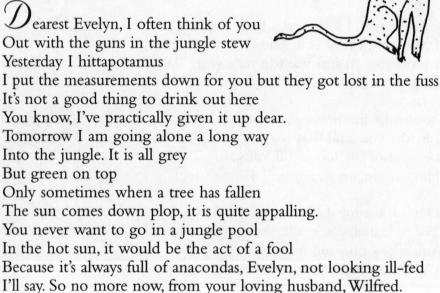

Dearest Evelyn, I often think of you
Out with the guns in the jungle stew
Yesterday I hittapotamus
I put the measurements down for you but they got lost in the fuss
It's not a good thing to drink out here
You know, I've practically given it up dear.
Tomorrow I am going alone a long way
Into the jungle. It is all grey
But green on top
Only sometimes when a tree has fallen
The sun comes down plop, it is quite appalling.
You never want to go in a jungle pool
In the hot sun, it would be the act of a fool
Because it's always full of anacondas, Evelyn, not looking ill-fed
I'll say. So no more now, from your loving husband, Wilfred.

Stevie Smith

A Birthday

My heart is like a singing bird
　Whose nest is in a watered shoot;
My heart is like an apple-tree
　Whose boughs are bent with thickset fruit;
My heart is like a rainbow shell
　That paddles in a halcyon sea;
My heart is gladder than all these
　Because my love is come to me.

Raise me a dais of silk and down;
　Hang it with vair and purple dyes;
Carve it in doves and pomegranates,
　And peacocks with a hundred eyes;
Work it in gold and silver grapes,
　In leaves and silver fleurs-de-lys;
Because the birthday of my life
　Is come, my love is come to me.

Christina Rossetti

Lovely Tracey

Dear Tracey,
I am sending
this letter to you
to show all my love
for you and care
and respect.
This letter is not
from Peter it is from
someone in class
two who cares and
loves you very much.
Perhaps one day
I may not like
you as much as I do
now so while you've
got some time to
show your love for
me just use it.
Don't be shy to say
it if you do I
will be really glad

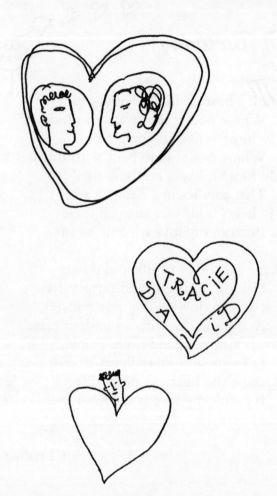

to know that you
love me. I have
only one thing to
say in nearly
everything I do I
always think of you
my beautiful girl.
    From *David*

David Phipps (9)

The Passionate Shepherd to his Love

Come live with me and be my love,
And we will all the pleasures prove,
That hills and valleys, dales and fields,
And all the craggy mountains yields.

There we will sit upon the rocks,
And see the shepherds feed their flocks,
By shallow rivers to whose falls
Melodious birds sing madrigals.

And I will make thee beds of roses
With a thousand fragrant posies,
A cap of flowers, and a kirtle
Embroidered all with leaves of myrtle;

A gown made of the finest wool
Which from our pretty lambs we pull;
Fair lined slippers for the cold,
With buckles of the purest gold;

A belt of straw and ivy buds,
With coral clasps and amber studs:
And if these pleasures may thee move,
Come live with me and be my love.

The shepherds' swains shall dance and sing
For thy delight each May morning:
If these delights thy mind may move,
Then live with me and be my love.

Christopher (Kit) Marlowe

I Luv Me Mudder

I luv me mudder an me mudder luvs me
we cum so far from over de sea,
we heard dat de streets were paved wid gold
Sometimes it's hot, sometimes it's cold,
I luv me mudder an me mudder luvs me
we try fe live in harmony
Yu might know her as Valerie
But to me she's just my mummy.

She shouts at me daddy so loud sometimes
She's always been a friend of mine
She's always doing de best she can
She works so hard down ina Englan,
She's always singin sum kinda song
She has big muscles an she very, very strong,
She likes pussycats an she luvs cashew nuts
An she don't bother wid no if an buts.

I luv me mudder an me mudder luvs me
we cum so far from over de sea,
we heard dat de streets were paved wid gold
Sometimes it's hot, sometimes it's cold,
I luv her and whatever we do
Dis is a luv I know is true,
My people, I'm talking to yu
Me an my mudder we luv yu too.

Benjamin Zephaniah

To the Spider in the Crevice
Behind the Toilet Door

i have left you four flies
three are in the freezer next to the joint of beef
the other is wrapped in christmas paper
tied with a pink ribbon
beside the ironing-table in the hall
should you need to contact me
in an emergency
the number's in the book
by the telephone.

p.s. i love you

Janet Sutherland

I Love You Because
(A Monster Duet)

You're fat and lumpy,
Ugly and grumpy,
Hairy, green and grimy,
You're big and smelly,
Sticky-out belly,
Oily, wet and shiny,
And that's why I love you.

You're cruel and grim,
You do people in,
Your eyes are small and beady,
You're nasty and sly,
You cheat and lie,
You're evil, mean and greedy,
And that's why I love you.

Colin McNaughton

To My Mother

When I looking into your eyes
when I looking at your face

I see the shadow
the shadow of my self

You are a woman
a woman to my soul

Wave upon waves
spirit
touching me
haunting me

that you are a woman
a woman to my heart

when I looking into your eyes
when I looking at your face

I see images
images
shadowing you to me

that you are a woman
a woman to my spirit

You gave life
you gave birth
you offer yourself

You are a woman
a woman that I love

You are a woman
a woman
You are my mother
my mother
You are a woman
a woman that I love
you are my mother

Tang Lin

21

i wanna
be yours

*l*et me be your vacuum cleaner
breathing in your dust
let me be your ford cortina
i will never rust
if you like your coffee hot
let me be your coffee pot
you can call the shots
i wanna be yours

let me be your raincoat
for those frequent rainy days
let me be your dreamboat
when you wanna sail away
let me be your teddy bear
take me with you everywhere
i don't care
i wanna be yours

let me be your electric meter
i will not run out
let me be the electric heater
you get cold without
let me be your setting lotion
hold your hair
with deep devotion
deep as the deep
atlantic ocean
that's how deep is my emotion
deep deep deep deep de deep deep
i don't wanna be hers
i wanna be yours

John Cooper Clarke

It was a Lover and His Lass

It was a lover and his lass,
  With a hey, and a ho, and a hey nonino,
That o'er the green corn-field did pass,
  In the spring time, the only pretty ring time,
When birds do sing, hey ding a ding, ding;
Sweet lovers love the spring.

Between the acres of the rye,
  With a hey, and a ho, and a hey nonino,
These pretty country folks would lie,
  In the spring time, the only pretty ring time,
When birds do sing, hey ding a ding, ding;
Sweet lovers love the spring.

This carol they began that hour,
  With a hey, and a ho, and a hey nonino,

How that life was but a flower
    In the spring time, the only pretty ring time,
When birds do sing, hey ding a ding, ding;
Sweet lovers love the spring.

And, therefore, take the present time
    With a hey, and a ho, and a hey nonino,
For love is crowned with the prime
    In the spring time, the only pretty ring time,
When birds do sing, hey ding a ding, ding;
Sweet lovers love the spring.

William Shakespeare

Untitled

I know you'll never love me
And this is why I cry,
I'll never feel your hand in mine
or hear you softly sigh.
I know you'll never miss me,
or notice that I've gone
To me, you are somebody
To you, I am no one
I know you'll never cry for me
The way I cry for you,
I know you'll never want me
So what can I do?
I know you'll never think of me
I'll never cross your mind.
You'll never waste a thought on me
I'll always find the time
I know you'll never look for me
The way I look for you.
Each face you see is different.
Each man I see is you,
I know you'll never lose your heart

The way that I lost mine
They say that time's a healer
To me there is no time,
I know you'll never love me
And this is why I cry.
Although my body's living
My heart is bound to die
I know you'll never love me.

H L Brazer

Home

Home's not merely four square walls,
   Though with pictures hung and gilded;
Home is where affection calls, –
   Fill'd with shrines the heart hath builded!
Home! – go watch the faithful dove,
   Sailing 'neath the heaven above us;
Home is where there's one to love;
   Home is where there's one to love us!

Home's not merely roof and room, –
   It needs something to endear it;
Home is where the heart can bloom, –
   Where there's some kind lip to cheer it!
What is home with none to meet, –
   None to welcome, none to greet us?
Home is sweet – and only sweet –
   When there's one we love to meet us!

Charles Swain

This Cat

This cat
she expects love.
Demands it
stalks it
feels she has a right to it.
She is not ashamed –
I wish I were more like this cat.

Gabriela Pearse

I'm in Love with the Weather Lady

I'm in love with the Weather Lady
I could sit here and watch her all day
I don't care if earthquakes are forecast
I just want to hear what she'll say

I'm in love with the Weather Lady
Can't wait until after the news
You can never see below her knees
Perhaps she doesn't wear shoes

I'm in love with the Weather Lady
Her smile drives the black clouds away
There's a deep depression if I miss her
A cold front that lasts through the day

I'm in love with the Weather Lady
I watch her through lunch-time and tea
I'm in love with the Weather Lady
But I don't think she knows about me.

Adrian Henri

First Love

Sarah's my girlfriend,
Without her I feel
Like a ball with no bounce,
A shoe with no heel,
An up with no down,
A snow with no flake,
A fish trying to swim
In a waterless lake.
Sarah's my girlfriend,
Without her I fear
I feel that I'm nowhere,
Especially not here.

Brian Patten

Extract from The Prophet (on love)

Love gives naught but itself and takes naught
but from itself.
Love possesses not nor would it be possessed;
For love is sufficient unto love.

When you love you should not say, 'God is in
my heart,' but rather, 'I am in the heart of God.'
And think not you can direct the course of love,
For love, if it finds you worthy, directs your course.

Love has not other desire but to fulfil itself.
But if you love and must needs have desires,
Let these be your desires:
To melt and be like a running brook that sings
its melody to the night.
To know the pain of too much tenderness.
To be wounded by your own understanding of
love.

Kahlil Gibran

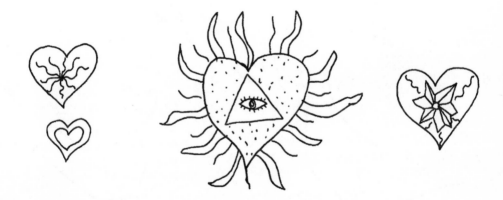

My Love for Thee is Like a Galah

If I compare love to birds
I'd say love was once a dove
cooing and close
Another time, love was a swan
full of grace
an owl, wide-eyed and wise
and a sparrow
an eagle, etc. etc.

But love has also been a chook
with its head on the block
and a hammer instead of a hatchet
And I remember love like a seagull
meeting a propeller -
not much left afterwards
And if, today, love is like
a squashed birdie corpse on the road of life
I live in trust that, of all the birds
love is most like the phoenix.

Lauren Williams

Lovesick

I'm scared of my own heart beat;
it's so loud someone might say
'who's on the drums?' and I'd blush
(not exactly beetroot) but blush
all the same.

I have these feelings.
I take them home from school
and tuck them up. In the morning
I say all the wrong things by accident
again and again.

Like, for instance, shouting *Miss*
in the middle of someone else saying
something. Usually Agnes MacNamara.
'In a minute,' says Miss. And I blush.
I hate MacNamara.

Miss is from Bangladesh and has
thick black hair, usually brushed
into one sleek pony. If I could tie the bow!
She has lovely eyes, dark pools.
Miss isn't married.

But I expect she will get married soon.
I think Mr Hudson wants to marry her.
Mr Hudson is always waiting in the corridor.
Him or that Agnes MacNamara.
Will I ever. Will I ever

Get older so that it doesn't hurt.
So that my heart doesn't hurt.
So that I don't spend all my time
with my fingers crossed and wishing:
Say something nice. Miss, Please. *Something*.

Jackie Kay

My Father's Hands

My father's hands
are beautiful, they can
fix this moth's wing and make
machines
they can mend the fuse when the world
goes dark
can make light swim and walls jump
in around me again
I can see my mother's face again.

You must take good care of them with
your finest creams
never let the nails break or
skin go dry, only those wise fingers
know how to fix the thing
that makes my doll cry and they make
small animals out of clay.

38

Never let blades or anything sharp
and hurtful near them
don't let bees or nettles
sting them don't let fire or burning oil
try them

My father's hands are beautiful, take
good care of them.

Jeni Couzyn

Love Song

*I*f I could write words
Like leaves on an autumn forest floor
What a bonfire my letters would make.
If I could speak words of water
You would drown when I said
'I love you'.

Spike Milligan

The Morning Walk

When Anne and I go out for
  a walk,
We hold each other's hand
  and talk
Of all the things we mean to do
When Anne and I are forty-two.

A. A. Milne

Traditional Indian Epigram

The friendship of the rogue
   or saint,
Like shade at dawn or shade
   at noon,
Starts large and slowly grows
   more faint,
Or starting faint, grows
   larger soon.

Absence is union dear
   when hearts are one;
Union is absence drear
   when love is done.

Yes, you were I, and I was you,
So fond the love that linked us two;
Alas, my friend, for friendships end!
Now I am I, and you are you.

                Anon.

The Crying Rain

I gave you a garland of hearts,
And you gave me a garland of thorns,
I spread flowers for you to walk on,
And you made me dance on glass,
For you I left my family and home,
And you did not give me any respect,
Now where can I go to?
I no longer have a home, and I no
    longer have you,
Where shall I take my love,
I cannot live without respect,
And without your love I cannot live,
My eternal love, do not give me thorns,
    let me soak myself in the rain of
        your love.

Komal Purwaha

25 Years of Togetherness

*H*appy Anniversary

25 Years, of togetherness,
25 Years, they may not be the best.
25 Years, of moving town to town
25 Years, of ups and downs.

25 Years, passed so swiftly by,
25 Years, time seems to fly.
25 Years ago we were on our own.
25 Years, and our children have grown.

25 Years went by and we are still here,
25 Years, and loved ones disappeared.
25 Years together we may not see again.
25 Years may bring inevitable change.

44

25 Years from now what will it be?
25 Years together again we may not see.
25 Years together we've spent,
25 Years, let's celebrate at full length.

25 Years not altogether the best
25 Years of perfect faithfulness
25 Years our loves together we share,
25 Years, I still love you my dear!

S G Grizzle

Hoping for a Dog

Dear God, I have a little dog,
He isn't really there, but in the night
When I'm alone I sometimes stroke his hair.
Dear God, I love my little dog who isn't really
So help him come out from my dreams
And let me keep him in my care.

Sophie Way (8)

Song

I had a dove and the sweet dove died
And I have thought it died of grieving:
O what could it grieve for? Its feet were tied,
With a silken thread of my own hand's weaving
Sweet little red feet! why should you die —
Why should you leave me, sweet bird! why?
You liv'd alone in the forest-tree,
Why, pretty thing! would you not live with me?
I kiss'd you oft and gave you white peas;
Why not live sweetly, as in the green trees?

John Keats

My Love Is

My love's not blonde
My love's not brown
My love is all around,
My love's beyond
My love's abound
My love is where I'm found,
My love's not black
My love's not white
My love's not in-between,
My love's not bad
My love's alright
My love's not red and green.
My love is true
My love is great
My love is very good,
My love is you
My love can't wait
My love is overstood,
My love is touch
My love is deep
My love keeps me alive,

My love's so much
My love's for keeps
And so hard to describe.

Benjamin Zephaniah

If the Earth

*I*f the Earth
were only a few feet in diameter,
floating a few feet above a field somewhere,
people would come from everywhere to marvel
at it. People would walk around it, marvelling at its
big pools of water, its little pools and the water flowing
between the pools. People would marvel at the bumps on
it, and the holes in it, and they would marvel at the very thin
layer of gas surrounding it and the water suspended in the gas.
The people would marvel at all the creatures walking around
the surface of the ball, and at the creatures in the water. The
people would declare it as sacred because it was the only one,
and they would protect it so that it would not be hurt. The
ball would be the greatest wonder known, and people would
come to pray to it, to be healed, to gain knowledge, to know
beauty and to wonder how it could be. People would
love it, and defend it with their lives because they
would somehow know that their lives, their own
roundness, could be nothing without it. If
the Earth were only a few feet in
diameter.

Steve Smith

I Once Thought a Lot of a Friend

I once thought a lot of a friend,
Who turned out to be, in the end,
   The most southerly part
   (As I'd feared from the start)
Of a horse with a northerly trend.

                Anon.

Stepmother

My stepmother
  is really nice.
She ought to wear
  a label.
I don't come in
  with a latch key, now –
my tea is on
  the table.
She doesn't nag at me
  or shout.
I often hear her
  singing.
I'm glad my dad
  had wedding bells –
and I hope
  they go on ringing.

Stepmothers
  in fairy tales
are hard and cold
  as iron.

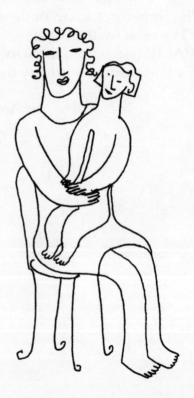

There isn't a lie
    they wouldn't tell,
or a trick
    they wouldn't try on.
But MY stepmother's
    warm and true;
she's kind, and cool,
    and clever –
Yes! I've a *wicked*
    stepmother –
and I hope she stays
    for ever!

Jean Kenward

I Love My Sandwich!

The Queen I am told
Loves cucumber sandwiches.
But I am not convinced you see.

I'm far too old to be taken in
By the cucumber's cool
And cheesy grin.

But I have nothing against
Our beloved Queen
I truly love her!

Nor do I begrudge
Her love for certain sandwiches.
After all she is the Queen!

Its the green between
Those royal slices
That do remind her
Of this green and pleasant land.

So, I'm cool Britannia!
You can keep that greeny in betweeny,
But my heart is given to another!

My beloved wears green eyelashes
And her skin is soft and ruby royal
And I would gladly wear her blushes.

I love the way she winks at me
From corner shop to market place,
And some do say that Queen Victoria
Would not allow tomatoes in her palace!

Yes, in my heart I love another
And when I kiss her
My heart is sweet as ketchup!

Ricardo Corvalan

The Soldier Loves His Rifle

The soldier loves his rifle,
  The scholar loves his books,
The farmer loves his horses,
  The film star loves her looks.
There's love the whole world over
  Wherever you may be;
Some lose their rest for gay Mae West,
  But you're my cup of tea.

Some talk of Alexander
  And some of Fred Astaire,
Some like their heroes hairy
  Some like them debonair,
Some prefer a curate
  And some an A.D.C.,
Some like a tough to treat 'em rough,
  But you're my cup of tea.

Some are mad on Airedales
    And some on Pekinese,
On tabby cats or parrots
    Or guinea pigs or geese.
There are patients in asylums
    Who think that they're a tree;
I had an aunt who loved a plant,
    But you're my cup of tea.

Some have sagging waistlines
    And some a bulbous nose
And some a floating kidney
    And some have hammer toes,
Some have tennis elbow
    And some have housemaid's knee,
And some I know have got B.O.,
    But you're my cup of tea.

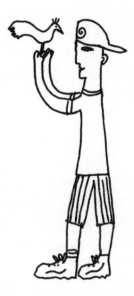

The blackbird loves the earthworm,
　　The adder loves the sun,
The polar bear an iceberg,
　　The elephant a bun,
The trout enjoys the river,
　　The whale enjoys the sea,
And dogs love most an old lamp-post,
　　But you're my cup of tea.

W. H. Auden

October 12th 1972

(for my Grandmother born 1872)

*T*he box we bear is cold
and surprisingly light.

One I love should weigh more.

Paul Hyland

He was . . .

*H*e was . . .
a boy who became
a man
a husband
a father.

He was . . .
a good goalie,
a rotten batsman,
not bad at darts.

He was . . .
second cornet in the works band;
a man who brought his pay-packet straight home
without stopping at the pub;
a man who enjoyed his dinner.

He was . . .
forgetful,
rarely on time,
sometimes tongue-tied,
at a loss for what to say.

He was . . .
always honest,
never sober at Christmas,
often puzzled by the world

He was . . .
. . . my dad.

John Cunliffe

For Rita with Love

You came home from school
on a special bus
full of people
who look like you
and love like you
and you met me
for the first time
and you loved me.
You love everybody
so much that it's not safe
to let you out alone.
Eleven years of love
and trust and time for you to learn
that you can't go on loving like this.
Unless you are stopped
you will embrace every person you see.
Normal people don't do that.
Some Normal people will hurt you
very badly because you do.

Cripples don't look nice
but you embrace them.
You kissed a wino on the bus
and he broke down and he cried
and he said 'Nobody has kissed me
for the last 30 years.'
But you did.
You touched my face
with your fingers and said
'I like you.'
The world will never
be ready for you.
Your way is right
and the world will
never be ready.

We could learn everything
that we need to know
by watching you
going to your special school
in your special bus –
full of people
who look like you
and love like you
and it's not safe
to let you out alone.
If you're not normal
there is very little hope
for the rest of us

Pat Ingoldsby

My Heart's in the Highlands

My heart's in the Highlands, my heart is not here;
My heart's in the Highlands a chasing the deer;
Chasing the wild deer, and following the roe;
My heart's in the Highlands, wherever I go. –

Farewell to the Highlands, farewell to the North;
The birth-place of Valour, the country of Worth;
Wherever I wander, wherever I rove,
The hills of the Highlands for ever I love. –

Farewell to the mountains high cover'd with snow;
Farewell to the Straths and green vallies below:
Farewell to the forests and wild-hanging woods;
Farewell to the torrents and loud-pouring floods. –

My heart's in the Highlands, my heart is not here
My heart's in the Highlands, a chasing the deer:
Chasing the wild deer, and following the roe;
My heart's in the Highlands, wherever I go. –

Robert Burns

Children

If children live with criticism
  they learn to condemn

If children live with hostility
  they learn to fight

If children live with ridicule
  they learn to be shy

If children live with shame
  they learn to feel guilty

If children live with tolerance
  they learn to be patient

If children live with encouragement
  they learn confidence

If children live with praise
  they learn to appreciate

If children live with fairness
    they learn justice

If children live with security
    they learn to have faith

If children live with approval
    they learn to like themselves

If children live with acceptance and friendship
    they learn to find love in the world

                              Anon.

Love's Philosophy

The fountains mingle with the river,
   And the rivers with the ocean,
The winds of heaven mix for ever
   With a sweet emotion;
Nothing in the world is single;
   All things by a law divine
In one another's being mingle –
   Why not I with thine?

See the mountains kiss high heaven,
   And the waves clasp one another;
No sister flower would be forgiven
   If it disdained its brother:
And the sunlight clasps the earth,
   And the moonbeams kiss the sea; –
What are all these kissings worth,
   If thou kiss not me?

Percy Bysshe Shelley

Love Bud

Do you carrot all for me?
My heart beets for you,
With your turnip nose
And your radish face.
You are a peach.
If we cantaloupe,
Lettuce marry;
Weed make a swell pear.

Anon.

Amo Ergo Sum

Because I love
The sun pours out its rays of living gold
Pours out its gold and silver on the sea.

Because I love
The earth upon her astral spindle winds
Her ecstasy-producing dance.

Because I love
Clouds travel on the winds through wide skies,
Skies wide and beautiful, blue and deep.

Because I love
Wind blows white sails,
The wind blows over flowers, the sweet wind blows.

Because I love
The ferns grow green, and green the grass, and green
The transparent sunlit trees.

Because I love
    Larks rise up from the grass
    And all the leaves are full of singing birds.

Because I love
    The summer air quivers with a thousand wings,
    Myriads of jewelled eyes burn in the light.

Because I love
    The iridescent shells upon the sand
    Take forms as fine and intricate as thought.

Because I love
    There is an invisible way across the sky,
    Birds travel by that way, the sun and moon
    And all the stars travel that path by night.

Because I love
    There is a river flowing all night long.

Because I love
    All night the river flows into my sleep,
    Ten thousand living things are sleeping in my arms,
    And sleeping wake, and flowing are at rest.

                                    Kathleen Raine

Me

'My nose is blue,
My teeth are green,
My face is like a soup tureen.
I look just like a lima bean.
I'm very, very lovely.
My feet are far too short
And long.
My hands are left and right
And wrong.
My voice is like the hippo's song.
I'm very, very,
Very, very,
Very, very
Lovely?'

Karla Kuskin

Serious Luv

Monday Morning

I really luv de girl dat's sitting next to me
I think she thinks like me an she's so cool,
I think dat we could live for ever happily
I want to marry her when I leave school.

She's de only one in school allowed to call me Ben
When she does Maths I luv de way she chews her pen,
When we are doing Art she's so artistic
In Biology she makes me heart beat so quick.

When we do Geography I go to paradise
She's helped me draw a map of Borneo twice!
Today she's going to help me take me books home
So I am going to propose to her when we're alone.

The next day

I used to luv de girl dat's sitting next to me
But yesterday it all came to an end,
She said that I should take love more seriously
An now I think I really luv her friend.

Benjamin Zephaniah

The Girl I Did Not Marry

When I was eighteen years of age
  I met a lovely girl;
She was so beautiful she made
  My thoughts and senses whirl.

Not only beautiful but kind,
  Intelligent as well;
Her smile was warm as India,
  Her voice a silver bell.

So gentle and so sensitive,
  She was the one for me;
We loved the same great melodies
  And peace and poetry.

In spring we wandered hand in hand
  Towards a treasured scene
To which I'd never taken her,
  Small paradise of green.

We climbed a gentle slope and then
  Walked through a little wood;
And there, below, were shining fields
  Where sheep and young lambs stood

Or danced or drifted on dry seas,
  Their bleatings frail or hoarse.
'When I see those,' my darling said,
  'I always smell mint sauce.'

                    Vernon Scannell

A Sojourn in Jhalda

Here I see people more clearly,
one by one.
Their hands,
one before, one after,
give love or hate
like a lump of earth.

In the clean silence
of trees, clouds
and the sun,
their words, like small saplings,
offer beauty.

Their sensuousness
shines – their women
with picked bosom
and half-hid thighs.

These people are birds.
With their method
of labour, there is
the loveliness of wings.

Here I am –
like a boat with sails.
So much air,
so much love to live with.

Subhas Chandra Saha

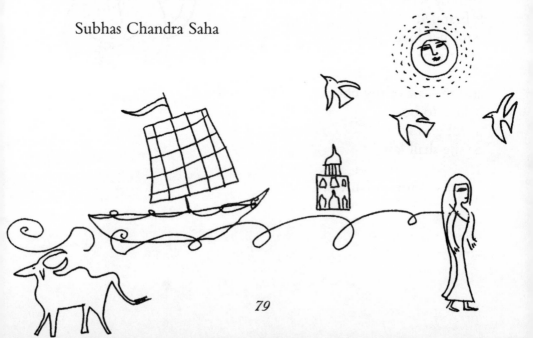

To My Dog

This gentle beast
This golden beast
laid her long chin
along my wrist

and my wrist
is branded
with her love
and trust

and the salt of my cheek
is hers to lick
so long as I
or she shall last

Adrian Mitchell

Motherless Baby

Motherless baby and babyless mother
Bring them together to love one another.

Christina Rossetti

Acts of Love

It was my cousin Harry –
ungainly, slurred of speech –
who showed me love.
He used to take me down the yard –
'You come with me, my duck.' –
to see his budgies,
show off his prize-cards
pinned in a crooked patchwork round the shed.

Then he would coax his favourite from the cage
cupping her breathing emerald
in his familiar hand.
I watched his stubby finger stroke her head,
linger among the lapping coverts of her wings,
explore the underdown of breast,
gentle her brittle claws.
I stood, forgotten,
while they shared a shred of song.
His thick lips brushed her bill
murmuring 'There's my beauty, now.'
I ached for someone
who would whisper so to me.

Sheila Simmons

I will Give My Love an Apple

I will give my love an apple without e'er a core,
I will give my love a house without e'er a door,
I will give my love a palace wherein she may be,
And she may unlock it without any key.

My head is the apple without e'er a core,
My mind is the house without e'er a door,
My heart is the palace wherein she may be,
And she may unlock it without any key.

Anon.

Love Poem for My Country

My country is for love
so say its valleys
where ancient rivers flow
the full circle of life
under the proud eye of birds
adorning the sky

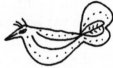

My country is for peace
so says the veld
where reptiles caress
its surface
with elegant motions
glittering in their pride

My country
is for joy
so talk the mountains

with baboons
hopping from boulder to boulder
in the majestic delight
of cliffs and peaks

My country
is for health and wealth
see the blue of the sea
and beneath
the jewels of fish
deep under the bowels of soil
hear
the golden voice
of a miner's praise
for my country

My country
is for unity
feel the millions
see their passion
their hands are joined together
there is hope in their eyes

we shall celebrate

Sandile Dikeni

April Rain Song

Let the rain kiss you.
Let the rain beat upon your head with silver liquid drops.
Let the rain sing you a lullaby.

The rain makes still pools on the sidewalk.
The rain makes running pools in the gutter.
The rain plays a little sleep-song on our roof at night –

And I love the rain.

Langston Hughes

Here lies the man Richard

*H*ere lies the man RICHARD,
  And MARY his wife;
Their surname was PRITCHARD,
  They lived without strife.
And the reason was plain:
  They abounded in riches,
They had no care or pain,
And the wife wore the breeches.

Chelmsford Cathedral, Essex

Not a Word

They walked the lane together,
The sky was dotted with stars.
They reached the rails together,
He lifted up the bars.
She neither smiled nor thanked him,
Because she knew not how,
For he was only the farmer's boy
And she was the Jersey cow!

Anon.

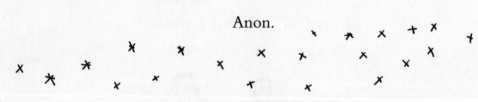

Honey I Love

I love
I love a lot of things, a whole lot of things
Like
My cousin comes to visit and you know he's from the South
'Cause every word he says just kind of slides out of his mouth
I like the way he whistles and I like the way he walks
But honey, let me tell you that I LOVE the way he talks
    I love the way my cousin talks
                        and

The day is hot and icky and the sun sticks to my skin
Mr Davis turns the hose on, everybody jumps right in
The water stings my stomach and I feel so nice and cool
Honey, let me tell you that I LOVE a flying pool
    I love to feel a flying pool
                    and

Renee comes out to play and brings her doll without a dress
I make a dress with paper and that doll sure looks a mess
We laugh so loud and long and hard the doll falls to the
    ground
Honey, let me tell you that I LOVE the laughing sound
    I love to make the laughing sound
                                and

My uncle's car is crowded and there's a lot of food to eat
We're going down the country where the church folks like to
    meet
I'm looking out the window at the cows and trees outside
Honey, let me tell you that I LOVE to take a ride
    I just love to take a family ride
                                and

My mama's on the sofa sewing buttons on my coat
I go and sit beside her, I'm through playing with my boat
I hold her arm and kiss it, 'cause it feels so soft and warm
Honey, let me tell you that I LOVE my mama's arm
    I love to kiss my mama's arm
                                and

It's not so late at night, but still I'm lying in my bed
I guess I need my rest, at least that's what my mama said
She told me not to cry 'cause she don't want to hear a peep
Honey, let me tell you I DON'T love to go to sleep
   I do not love to go to sleep

But I love
I love a lot of things, a whole lot of things
And honey,
I love you, too.

Eloise Greenfield

Extract from The Prophet (on marriage)

*L*ove one another, but make not a bond of love:

   Let it rather be a moving sea between the shores of your souls.

   Fill each other's cup but drink not from one cup.

   Give one another of your bread but eat not from the same loaf.

   Sing and dance together and be joyous, but let each one of you be alone,

   Even as the strings of a lute are alone though they quiver with the same music.

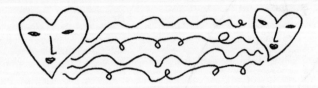